BIBLE PEOPLE
QUIZ BOOK

Erma Reynolds

BAKER BOOK HOUSE
Grand Rapids, Michigan

1. ACCUSERS

1. Who accused his brothers of being spies?

2. What king accused his servants of conspiring against him?

3. Who accused Paul of polluting the temple?

4. What punishment was meted out to those who accused Daniel to Darius?

5. In which of Jesus' parables did a rich man accuse his accountant of stealing?

6. What tradesman accused Paul of hurting the sale of handcrafted goods?

7. What captain of the guard accused Jeremiah of defecting to the Chaldeans?

8. Who accused Moses and Aaron of exalting themselves above God's assembly?

9. What sect accused the disciples of law-breaking by harvesting grain on the Sabbath?

10. Who accused Naboth of blasphemy and had him stoned?

2. ANGRY PEOPLE

1. Who was hot with anger when he left the presence of a stubborn king?

2. What soldier became angry because his young brother left sheep-tending to come to a battle site?

3. What man became so angry he cut a yoke of oxen into pieces?

4. What king became angry with three men and had them thrown into a fiery furnace?

5. Who became angry because God paid more attention to his brother than to him?

6. Who became angry with his mule and beat it with a stick?

7. What king left a banquet in a rage and went into the palace garden?

8. Who became so angry with his father he left the dinner table without eating?

3. AUTHORS

1. Who is the first author to be mentioned in the Bible?
2. Who was told in a vision that what he saw he was to write in a book?
3. What preacher in a synagogue was handed a book written by the prophet Isaiah to read?
4. Who said his tongue was "the pen of a ready writer"?
5. Which author gave a copy of his book to a man, told him to tie a stone to it, and throw it into a river?
6. Who wished his words could be written and then printed in a book?
7. Who was the author of 3,000 proverbs?
8. Who wrote about the rights and duties of a kingdom and laid the book before God?
9. Who was the author of the Old Testament book that contains only one chapter?
10. What prophet wrote some of Solomon's biography?

4. BABIES

1. What baby was adopted by a princess?
2. What baby's weaning was celebrated with a great feast?
3. What baby's nurse was his mother?
4. What baby's nurse was his grandmother?
5. What twin baby boy was born grasping his brother's heel?
6. What baby was given a name by his dying mother, but had it changed by his father?
7. Who wished he had died when he was a baby?
8. Who was the first baby born on earth?
9. What baby's birth was announced by angels?
10. What baby was given in answer to a prayer?

5. BEAUTIFUL PEOPLE

1. What king wanted to show off his queen's beauty to banquet guests?

2. Who was beautiful "from the sole of his foot even to the crown of his head"?

3. What young shepherd was handsome and had ruddy cheeks?

4. Whose daughters were said to be the fairest in the land?

5. What girl was chosen to be queen as the result of a beauty contest?

6. What beautiful girl filled a pitcher at a well and gave a stranger a drink?

7. Who was the most handsome man in Israel, a head and shoulders taller than anyone else?

8. What beautiful woman caught the eye of a king as he strolled on a palace roof?

9. What slave was described as being "a goodly person, and well favoured"?

10. What girl was so graceful and beautiful, a man was willing to work seven years to get her for his wife?

6. BEREAVED PEOPLE

1. What bereaved father, whose two sons had been killed by fire, was forbidden to mourn for them?

2. What woman, whose husband and two sons had died, changed her name to one that meant "bitter"?

3. What prophet was instructed by God not to weep for his dead wife?

4. What bereaved son asked permission of a king to return his father's body to Canaan?

5. What bereaved husband purchased a cave for his wife's burial place?

6. What man, when told his ten sons and daughters had been killed, shaved his head, tore his mantle, and fell to the ground?

7. What bereaved king mourned for his dead son, wishing he could have died in his place?

8. What bereaved father, whose little daughter had died, was told by Jesus, "Weep not; she is not dead but sleepeth"?

9. What bereaved husband set a pillar upon his wife's grave that is still there today?

10. What bereaved mother guarded the bodies of her two dead sons through a harvest season?

7. BLESSERS

Each person listed in the left-hand column gave a blessing to a person, or persons, listed at the right. See if you can match them.

1. Isaac	a. Mary and Joseph
2. Joshua	b. Elkanah and his wife
3. Laban	c. Children of Israel
4. Melchizedek	d. Caleb
5. David	e. Jael
6. Moses	f. Pharaoh
7. Simeon	g. Jacob
8. Eli	h. Sons and daughters
9. Jacob	i. Barzillai
10. Deborah	j. Abram

8. BLIND PEOPLE

This quiz is about Scripture people who had eye problems. Select the correct name from the choice of three.

1. What Ammonite king threatened to put out the right eye of men he defeated?
(a) Nahash   (b) Nahamini   (c) Nahari

2. What blind prophet was visited by a woman in disguise?
(a) Ahaziah   (b) Abijah   (c) Ahijah

3. When surrounded by an enemy, who prayed to God to strike them with blindness?
(a) Elijah   (b) Elishaphat   (c) Elisha

4. What sorcerer became blind as punishment for evil doings?
(a) Elymas   (b) Simon Magus   (c) Witch of Endor

5. Who saw two angels strike with blindness a group of men who were trying to break into his house?
(a) Job   (b) Lot   (c) Hod

6. What half-blind father was deceived by his son?
(a) Eli   (b) Jacob   (c) Isaac

7. What king, overtaken by an enemy army, had his eyes put out?
(a) Zedekiah   (b) Zechariah   (c) Zerahiah

8. What blind beggar had his eyesight restored by Jesus?
(a) Barabbas   (b) Barnabas   (c) Bartimaeus

9. Who was blind for three days after being converted?
(a) Simon   (b) Paul   (c) Jailer at Philippi

10. What blind man pushed down temple pillars, killing thousands of people?
(a) Samson   (b) Adino   (c) Eleazar

9. BOYS

1. What five-year-old boy was dropped by his nurse and lamed for life?

2. What boy had a city named for him by his father?

3. What boy carried wood to an altar to burn himself as a sacrificial offering?

4. What twelve-year-old boy astounded temple priests with his intelligence?

5. What teen-age boy was given a coat of variegated colors?

6. What two boys were taken to visit their dying grand-father?

7. What boy had a coat made for him each year by his mother?

8. What boy was only seven years old when he became king of Judah?

9. What dead boy, after receiving attention from Elisha, sneezed seven times and opened his eyes?

10. What boy, banished into the wilderness with his mother, almost died of thirst?

10. BROTHERS

First unscramble the names listed in the right-hand column. Then match the brothers.

1. Solomon passed a death sentence on this brother.

   a. EOJSHP

2. Abihu and this brother were killed because they offered strange fire to God.

   b. COJAB

3. Seth had this murderer for a brother.

   c. SAJEM

4. Aaron acted as a mouthpiece for this brother.

   d. ABDAN

5. Peter and this brother were fishermen.

   e. IADVD

6. Esau hated this brother because he stole his blessing.

   f. ANIOJADH

7. Eliab rebuked this brother for leaving sheep unattended.

   g. MOSNEI

8. John and this brother discontinued mending nets to follow Jesus.

   h. EOSMS

9. Judah asked this brother to help him fight Canaanites.

   i. NACI

10. Benjamin was given a large portion of food by this brother.

    j. EWADNR

11. BUILDERS

1. Who bought a hill and built a city on it?
2. Who built a house and booths for his cattle?
3. Who built fortified towers in Jerusalem?
4. Who said, "As a wise master builder I have laid the foundation, and another buildeth thereon"?
5. What divinely inspired craftsman built much of a Tabernacle?
6. Who built cities in mountains, and castles and towers in forests?
7. Who was the first shipbuilder?
8. What king was an expert in the building of waterworks?
9. Who was the first city builder?
10. What builder of walls had to equip his workers with a tool in one hand and weapon in the other?

12. BUSINESS PEOPLE

1. Who had extensive business dealings in grain?
2. Who went in the tent-making business with a man and wife team?
3. What prophet set up a widow in the oil business?
4. What woman was a success in the purple-dyed cloth trade?
5. What two kings went into shipbuilding together?
6. What silversmith claimed that because of Paul the sales volume of silver shrines was declining?
7. What prophet gave a comprehensive inventory of the exports and imports of Tyre?
8. What tax collector abandoned his business to follow Jesus?
9. What king was in the lumber business?
10. What king engaged in the business of buying and selling linen yarn?

13. BUYERS

Each person listed in the left-hand column bought one of the items listed on the right. See if you can match them.

1. Potiphar
2. Abraham
3. David
4. Joseph
5. Chief Priests
6. Boaz
7. Joseph of Arimathaea

8. Jacob
9. Omri
10. Mary Magdalene, Mary, Salome

a. Cave for burial use
b. Land of Egypt
c. Wife
d. Fine linen
e. Bond servant
f. Parcel of a field
g. Threshing floor and oxen
h. Hill of Samaria
i. Sweet spices

j. Potters field

14. CAPTAINS

1. What captain of the host was a leper?
2. Who was David's chief captain that killed 800 men in a single battle?
3. What captain was murdered by a woman?
4. This first cousin of King Saul was also captain of his boat.
5. Who was the Roman captain who rescued Paul from Jerusalem Jews?
6. Who was the captain of the guard who bought Joseph?
7. What "mighty man of valour" was asked by the elders of Gilead, "Come, and be our captain, that we may fight with the children of Ammon"?
8. What refugee became captain of about 400 men?
9. What relative of David was appointed to be captain of the host in place of Joab?
10. What captain of the guard burned all the houses in Jerusalem when that city was taken?

15. CAPTIVES

1. What man, taken captive by enemy kings, was rescued by his uncle?

2. What king, after being in captivity for thirty-seven years, was released from prison and given a daily allowance of food for his lifetime?

3. What captive prophet mingled with other captives by the river Chebar?

4. What captive interpreted a king's dreams so well he was put in charge of a nationwide farm program?

5. At Babylon what young captive of good birth was selected as a trainee for state service?

6. What captive king had his eyes put out and then was imprisoned?

7. What group of captives hung their harps on willow trees?

8. What king was taken captive by Nebuchadnezzar and deported to Babylon along with his mother, wives, and officers?

9. Which book of the Bible gives the story of exiles returned to their own land again after years of captivity?

10. What Jewish captive was advanced to a high position in King Ahaseurus' kingdom?

16. CATTLEMEN

1. Who ploughed with twelve pair of oxen?
2. What two men helped each other find pasture land for their cattle?
3. Who had thousands of his cattle and camels stolen?
4. Who made booths for his cattle?
5. What two cattlemen had to break up their partnership because of trouble between their herdsmen?
6. What prophet was a herdsman?
7. Who owned so many cattle that the Philistines became envious and they stopped up his wells?
8. What cattleman used his son-in-law as hired help to care for his herds?
9. Who was Saul's chief herdsman?
10. Who was the first of the cattlemen?

17. CONCEALERS

Each person listed at the left hid something that is mentioned in the right-hand column. Match each concealer with the item hid.

1. Jochebed
2. Obadiah
3. Jeremiah
4. Jacob

5. Moses
6. Rahab
7. Servant in a parable

8. Achan

9. Rachel
10. Jehosheba

a. Battle spoils under a tent
b. Idols in a bag
c. Baby by a riverside
d. Little prince in a temple storeroom
e. Money in the earth
f. Body in sand
g. Earrings under an oak tree
h. One hundred prophets in caves
i. Two spies on a housetop
j. Stones in clay near a palace

18. CONSPIRATORS

Match the conspirator(s) listed on the left with the person plotted against, listed on the right.

1. Absalom	a. Elah
2. Servants	b. Joseph
3. Delilah	c. David
4. Gaal	d. Jesus
5. Jews	e. Joash
6. Jehu	f. Abimelech
7. Brothers	g. Samson
8. Ahimelech	h. Joram
9. Pharisees	i. Paul
10. Zimri	j. Saul

19. CONVERTS

1. What man, who suddenly became blind, became a convert when he regained his sight?

2. On the day of Pentecost, how many people were converted?

3. What Roman centurion was converted by Peter?

4. Who converted an Ethiopian eunuch?

5. Who was told he would become a convert after meeting a band of prophets playing musical instruments?

6. What sorcerer became a convert?

7. What king recovering from insanity became a convert?

8. What "seller of purple" became a convert?

9. To which of his disciples did Jesus say, "But I have prayed for thee, that thy faith fail not; and when thou art converted, strengthen thy brethren"?

10. What proconsul became a convert after seeing a sorcerer punished with blindness?

20. COURAGEOUS PEOPLE

Listed in the left-hand column are some courageous people. Match each person with his instance of bravery listed at the right.

1. Gideon

   a. Persisted in praying, even though it meant being thrown to lions.

2. Aaron

   b. Dared to ask Pilate for Jesus' body.

3. Three Hebrews

   c. During a battle in which he was deserted by fellow soldiers, he alone beat back the enemy.

4. Benaiah

   d. During a plague he dared to mingle with the stricken people, to make atonement for them with God.

5. Paul

   e. Refused to run from danger and take refuge in a temple.

6. Joseph of Arimathaea

   f. Attacked a vast army with only 300 men.

7. Nehemiah

   g. Dared to face an enemy giant, armed with only a sling and staff.

8. Shammah

   h. Killed two lion-like men, a lion, and Egyptian warrior.

9. David

   i. Refused to bow to an image, even though it meant death in a fiery furnace.

10. Daniel

   j. Went to Jerusalem, even though he knew imprisonment awaited him there.

21. COVENANTERS

In the left-hand column are people who made a covenant. At the right are articles, or procedures, used to ratify the covenant. See if you can match them.

1. Solomon - Hiram
2. Hannah - God
3. Asa - Benhadad
4. Rahab - Spies

5. Abraham - Abimelech
6. Judas Iscariot - Chief priests

7. Jonathan - David
8. Nahash - Jabeshnites
9. Noah - God
10. Laban - Jacob

a. Rainbow
b. Gift of gold and silver
c. Loss of right eyes
d. Child whose hair would never be cut
e. Food for a household

f. Robe, sword, bow, girdle
g. Ewe lambs
h. Pile of stones
i. Thirty pieces of silver
j. Scarlet cord

22. COVETOUS PEOPLE

1. Who coveted spoils taken from an enemy?
2. Who coveted a vineyard?
3. Who said, "I have coveted no man's silver, or gold, or apparel"?
4. What servant coveted gifts his master had refused?
5. Who coveted "the wages of unrighteousness"?
6. What former sorcerer coveted the gift of the Holy Ghost?
7. What sect did Jesus denounce as being covetous?
8. What governor of Judaea coveted bribe money?
9. Who coveted fruit?
10. Who coveted money received from selling property?

23. COWARDS

Match the cowards in the left-hand column with their particular demonstration of cowardice listed at the right.

1. Samuel

a. He proved to be a coward by yielding to a crowd that wanted him to make them an idol.

2. Adam

b. They showed a cowardly streak during a storm at sea.

3. Israelites

c. He was afraid to admit he knew Jesus.

4. Jacob

d. He chose the night time to destroy an idolatrous altar, afraid of the consequences if he was found out.

5. Disciples

e. Cowardice showed up when a giant appeared.

6. Abraham

f. Fearful of a crowd, this coward condemned an innocent man to death.

7. Peter

g. This cowardly husband shifted responsibility for disobedience upon his wife.

8. Gideon

h. Fearful of being killed by Egyptians, he told his wife to pretend she was his sister.

9. Aaron

i. Because he was afraid of his father-in-law, he stole away with his family and household goods.

10. Pilate

j. He displayed cowardice when he told God he was afraid to anoint a new king.

24. CRIMINALS

Match each person listed in the left-hand column with his crime listed at the right.

1. Ehud	a. Kidnapping
2. Samson	b. Theft
3. Gibeonites	c. Forgery
4. Micah	d. Bribery
5. Absalom	e. Extortion
6. Samuel's Sons	f. Fraud
7. Benjaminites	g. Conspiracy
8. Jezebel	h. Swindling
9. Rich Jews	i. Arson
10. Ananias	j. Murder

25. CRUEL PEOPLE

1. What cruel queen murdered all her grandchildren except one?
2. What mistress was cruel to her maid?
3. What king passed an edict, ordering the death of babies under age two?
4. Which of Jacob's sons did he describe as being cruel?
5. What Egyptian ruler cruelly mistreated Israelites?
6. What king had Zedekiah blinded and imprisoned for the remainder of his life?
7. What cruel woman demanded the head of John the Baptist?
8. What successor to a throne threatened to punish his subjects with scorpions?
9. Who hired assassins to slaughter seventy of his half brothers?
10. Who sacrificed his oldest son as a burnt offering on a wall?

26. DAUGHTERS

Match each daughter in the left-hand column, to her father, listed at the right.

1. Michal
2. Tamar
3. Rebekah
4. Abigail
5. Dinah
6. Achsah
7. Leah
8. Miriam
9. Zipporah
10. Jemima

a. Jesse
b. Reuel
c. David
d. Laban
e. Saul
f. Job
g. Bethuel
h. Jacob
i. Amram
j. Caleb

27. DECEIVERS

1. Who pretended to be insane to deceive King Achish?

2. What servant tried to deceive his master and was stricken with leprosy as punishment?

3. What woman pretended to be a mourner to deceive David?

4. Who deceived his half-blind father by wearing goat skins on his hands?

5. What two men were deceitful, pretending their wives were their sisters?

6. Who deceived a king, telling him he had a secret message for him, and then killed him?

7. Who tried to deceive Peter by lying about a sale of property?

8. Who deceived a bridegroom on his wedding night?

9. What woman was given 1,100 pieces of silver to deceive a man into revealing the secret of his strength?

10. Who deceived relatives, pretending he did not know them, and accused them of being spies?

28. DISCIPLES

1. Who was the first disciple to whom Jesus said, "Follow me"?
2. Who served as treasurer for the disciples?
3. Which disciple was a tax collector before joining Jesus' twelve?
4. What was Thomas' other name?
5. What was Thaddaeus' other name?
6. Which disciple was present at the miraculous feeding of the 5,000?
7. Which disciple tried to walk on water?
8. Which disciple did Jesus first see under a fig tree?
9. Who was the only disciple present at Jesus' crucifixion?
10. Which disciple was martyred by Herod?

29. DISEASED PEOPLE

The people listed at the left were afflicted with a variety of diseases. Match them to their ailments listed at the right.

1. Asa	a. Boils
2. Job	b. Worms
3. Naaman	c. Foot trouble
4. Nabal	d. Palsy
5. Lazarus	e. Insomnia
6. Jehoram	f. Heart attack
7. Herod	g. Leprosy
8. Simon's mother-in-law	h. Intestinal disease
9. Aeneas	i. Sores
10. Hezekiah	j. Fever

30. DISGUISED PEOPLE

1. Who disguised himself when he went to visit a witch?

2. What queen disguised herself when she went to visit a prophet?

3. To trick Joshua, who used a disguise of old clothing?

4. What son was disguised to fool his father?

5. What disguised king was fatally injured by archers during a battle?

6. What was the disguise of the prophet who waited by the roadside for the king of Israel?

7. What king went into battle disguised as an ordinary soldier?

8. What disguise did false prophets use that Jesus warned against?

9. Who "made himself strange" to his brothers so they would not recognize him?

10. What disguise did Joab have a woman use so she could meet with King David?

31. DOUBTERS

1. What woman made a long trip to check on a man because she doubted reports she had heard about him?

2. What did God have Moses do to dispel doubt among the Israelites?

3. Which apostle is known as "the doubter"?

4. What elderly man, because he doubted he would become a father, was stricken dumb?

5. What maid servant was doubted when she said Peter was at the door?

6. Who tried to walk on water, but because of doubt began to sink?

7. Who doubted he could be cured of leprosy by washing in a river?

8. Who said, "Neither be ye of doubtful mind"?

32. DREAMERS

1. Who complained that God frightened him with dreams and nightmares?

2. Who dreamed of a tree that reached to heaven?

3. Who overheard a soldier's dream about hard bread overturning a tent?

4. Who had a dream of angels going up and down a ladder?

5. Who was so frightened by a character in his dream that his hair stood on end?

6. In a dream God gave this man a choice of anything he wanted, and he chose wisdom.

7. What king dreamed of seven fat cows that came out of a river?

8. What man, because of a dream, arose in the middle of the night and set off on a trip with his wife and child?

9. Who dreamed that the sun, moon, and stars bowed to him?

10. What man was warned about his son-in-law in a dream?

33. ELDERLY PEOPLE

Match each aged person listed at the left with his description at the right.

1. Caleb

a. This bedridden, aged king was always cold no matter how many blankets were heaped upon him.

2. Asa

b. This 147-year-old man made his son promise to bury him in Egypt.

3. Methuselah

c. This 85-year-old man asked to be given a mountain.

4. Barzilla

d. This leader was still hale and hearty when he died at age 120 years.

5. Abraham

e. This king "in the time of his old age was diseased in his feet."

6. Solomon

f. This 80-year-old man passed up an invitation to live in a king's house because of his advanced age.

7. Jacob

g. This man lived longer than any other man in history.

8. Eli

h. This king in his old age had his heart turned from God by his idolatrous wives.

9. Moses

i. This man at 99 years of age had his name changed.

10. David

j. This old man fell backward from a seat and broke his neck.

34. ENEMIES

1. Who became an enemy of David because of jealousy?
2. Who was called "the Jews' enemy"?
3. Who were the two enemies of Nehemiah?
4. Who was an enemy of his father?
5. What enemy demanded the surrender of Jabesh-Gilead and the removal of the right eyes of its men?
6. What queen was an enemy of Elijah?
7. What enemy of David threatened him with curses, stones, and dirt?
8. What man did the Philistines consider their enemy?
9. Who was his brother's enemy?
10. Who had presidents and princes as his enemy?

35. ENVIOUS PEOPLE

Match each person in the left-hand column to the person he or she envied listed at the right.

1. Joshua
2. Haman
3. Presidents & Princes
4. Rachel
5. Saul
6. Laban's Sons
7. Miriam
8. Chief Priests
9. Cain
10. Philistines

a. Mordecai
b. Leah
c. Jacob
d. Moses
e. Eldad & Medad
f. Jesus
g. Daniel
h. Abel
i. Isaac
j. David

36. ESCAPEES

Each person listed at the left made an escape. Match them to their means of escape listed at the right.

1. David
2. Saul (Paul)
3. Noah
4. Ahimaaz & Jonathan
5. Apostles
6. Israelites
7. Jeremiah
8. Spies
9. Ben-Hadad
10. Jonah

a. Drawn up from a dungeon by rotten rags
b. Let down from a window by a rope
c. Found a dry path through a sea
d. Let down a wall in a basket
e. A big fish spit him up
f. Used a horse for escape
g. His wife put an idol in his bed so he could escape
h. Entered an ark
i. An angel opened prison gates
j. Hid in a well

37. EXILES

1. Who was told to "get thee out of thy country . . . unto a land that I will shew thee"?
2. Who became an exile because of a jealous mistress?
3. Who was the first exile of Scripture times?
4. Who was sold into exile?
5. What exiled captain from Jerusalem refused to leave David when he fled from Absalom?
6. Who became an exile because he killed his brother?
7. What servant of Solomon became an exile because he had revolted against the king?
8. Who became an exile to escape a brother who wanted to kill him?
9. In what king's reign were Jewish exiles repatriated?
10. Who brought back the exiled Absalom?

38. THE FAITHFUL

Match the people in the left-hand column to the way they demonstrated their faith in God.

1. Joshua   a. Got ready for a flood, following God's instructions.

2. Moses   b. Made a dangerous journey to Jerusalem without military escort.

3. David   c. Was willing to offer his son as a burnt offering.

4. Elijah   d. Led the Israelites through the Red Sea to escape bondage.

5. Asa   e. Knew he could rebuild a wall with God's help.

6. Abraham   f. Knew God would bring the Israelites into a land of milk and honey.

7. Noah   g. Knew by following God's orders he could take Jericho.

8. Ezra   h. Faced a giant without fear.

9. Caleb & Joshua   i. Knew God would allow him to defeat an army of a million men.

10. Nehemiah   j. Knew he could win a contest with priests of Baal.

39. FARMERS

1. Who grew a tremendous crop that was 100 times the grain he sowed?
2. What king "loved husbandry"?
3. Who was the first "tiller of the soil"?
4. Who built booths for his cattle?
5. What farmer winnowed his barley at night?
6. Who ploughed with twelve yoke of oxen?
7. Who threshed grain secretly in a wine press?
8. What king put ten men in charge of his farm activities?
9. What farmers had their plowshares sharpened by Philistine smiths?
10. What prophet was a herdsman?

40. FASTERS

In the left-hand column are people who fasted. Listed at the right are why, when, or where they fasted. See if you can match them.

1. Moses	a. Before having a dangerous interview with a king.
2. Ahab	b. Because he had put a man in a lions' den.
3. Nehemiah	c. As a way to worship God.
4. Jesus	d. After being reproached by Elijah over his wickedness.
5. David	e. Because of idolatrous marriages of returned exiles.
6. Darius	f. While with God on a mountain.
7. Ezra	g. While having visions.
8. Anna	h. While being tempted by the devil.
9. Daniel	i. After hearing about the run-down condition of Jerusalem.
10. Esther	j. At the time of his child's sickness.

41. FATHERS

Match each father listed in the left-hand column, to his description at the right.

1. Job

a. He burned his son alive as a sacrifice to heathen gods.

2. Gideon

b. He became a father when 100 years old.

3. Abraham

c. He introduced his eight sons to a prophet.

4. Reuel

d. He had twin sons.

5. Isaac

e. He named a city after his son.

6. Jair

f. He had four spinster daughters who were prophetesses.

7. Cain

g. He had the fairest daughters in the land.

8. Ahaz

h. He had seven daughters who were shepherdesses.

9. Philip

i. He had 70 sons.

10. Jesse

j. He had 30 sons who had 30 cities.

42. FIRST DOERS

This quiz is to test your knowledge of Scripture people who were first to do things. Match each person in the left-hand column to his deed listed at the right.

1. Cain		a.	First to be mentioned as going hunting.
2. Saul		b.	First song writer.
3. Jacob		c.	First ship builder.
4. Jubal		d.	First to serve as king.
5. Abraham		e.	First gardener.
6. Noah		f.	First machinist in brass and iron.
7. Nimrod		g.	Built the first city.
8. Moses		h.	First to erect a monument to the memory of the dead.
9. Tubal-Cain		i.	First land purchaser.
10. Adam		j.	First inventor of musical instruments.

43. FRIENDS

1. Who befriended Paul when he was a prisoner?
2. Who were Job's three friends who sat with him for seven days and nights?
3. What two men experienced an immediate bond of friendship?
4. Who became a false friend to David?
5. What three people were warm personal friends of Jesus?
6. What king and governor, who had been enemies, became friends during a trial?
7. What man and wife were friends of Paul?
8. What king was a friend and business associate of a father and son over a period of years?
9. Who was called "the friend of God"?
10. Who, when he got a promotion from a king, requested that his three friends be promoted also?

44. FRIGHTENED PEOPLE

In the left-hand column are Bible people who experienced fear. At the right is the event that made them afraid. See if you can match them.

1.	Israelites	a.	Angel with a sword
2.	Joseph's Brothers	b.	High waves
3.	Saul	c.	Thunderstorm
4.	Peter, James, John	d.	Man's shining face
5.	Eliphaz	e.	Money in a sack
6.	Belshazzar	f.	Voice coming out of a bright cloud
7.	Peter	g.	Son-in-law
8.	Nebuchadnezzar	h.	Handwriting on a wall
9.	Aaron	i.	A spirit
10.	David	j.	Dream

45. FUGITIVES

1. What high priest became a fugitive because Saul was killing priests?

2. Who had to become a fugitive because he murdered his brother?

3. Who became a fugitive because of a jealous mistress?

4. Who became a fugitive because he stole his brother's blessing?

5. Who became a fugitive because he killed an Egyptian?

6. After a warning in a dream, who became a fugitive with his wife and child?

7. What king's son became a fugitive after having his half-brother killed?

8. What fugitive, afraid of what King Achish might do to him, pretended to be insane?

9. Who became a fugitive to escape being killed by Solomon?

10. How were fugitives from Ephraim's army detected?

46. GIANTS

These questions concern some of the "giants in the earth" (Gen. 6:4) of Bible times.

1. What Philistine giant challenged Israelite armies and was killed by a lad armed with a slingshot?

2. What giant who tried to kill David was killed by Abishai?

3. What man, armed with only a staff, pulled a spear from a 7½ foot giant and used it to kill him?

4. What race of giants did Moses warn the Israelites they would encounter after crossing the river Jordan?

5. Who killed Lahmi, the brother of Goliath?

6. Who saw giants so large that it made them feel like grasshoppers in comparison?

7. What oversized king, the last survivor of a tribe of giants, had a huge bed?

8. Who killed a giant who had six fingers on each hand and six toes on each foot?

9. What tribe inherited the "valley of the giants"?

10. How many offspring of the "giant in Gath" were killed by David's troops?

47. GUESTS

Fill in each blank with the name of a guest who fits the accompanying clue.

1. _____ was the guest of two sisters.

2. _____ was the guest of honor at a dinner party given by Samuel.

3. _____ was the guest for three days of Publius, governor of Melita.

4. _____ was provided with a guest room prepared especially for his visits.

5. _____ as a dinner guest was given a serving five times larger than that served to the other guests.

6. _____ was accused of inhospitality because he failed to kiss a guest and anoint his head with oil.

7. _____ was invited as a dinner guest and ended up living with his host and marrying his daughter.

8. _____ was invited to become a permanent guest at David's table.

9. _____ asked Rebekah, "Is there room in thy father's house for us to lodge in?"

10. _____ were guests of a woman they had converted.

48. HEROIC PEOPLE

The people listed at the left took a brave part in a Scripture event. See if you can match each person to the courageous act.

1. David

a. Conquered a city and won a wife for his reward.

2. Esther

b. Armed with only a tent pin, she killed an enemy captain.

3. Three Mighty Men

c. Attacked the armies of Midianites and Amalekites with only 300 men.

4. Shammah

d. Threw a millstone on the head of a military leader who was about to burn a city and killed him.

5. Woman of Thebes

e. Risked death in going before a king on behalf of Jesus.

6. Gideon

f. Broke through Philistine ranks to get a drink of water for a leader.

7. Othniel

g. When deserted by his soldiers, he stood alone in a field and beat back enemy Philistines.

8. Shamgar

h. Accompanied by only an armor bearer, he climbed into an enemy garrison and killed about twenty men.

9. Jael

i. Killed a giant that was challenging the Israelite forces.

10. Jonathan

j. Killed 600 Philistines with an ox goad, thereby saving Israel from disaster.

49. HELPERS

1. What woman helped the poor and needy?
2. What two men helped Moses win a battle by holding up his tired hands?
3. Who helped two spies make their escape?
4. What man and woman were Paul's "helpers in Christ"?
5. What military man told Abishai that if enemy Ammonites proved too strong for him to defeat, he would come and help him?
6. Who helped a man who had been attacked by bandits?
7. What fugitive helped some girls water their flocks?
8. Who said, "I delivered the poor that cried, and the fatherless, and him that had none to help him"?
9. Who helped Jesus carry the cross?
10. What prophetess agreed to help a military leader in an attack on the enemy?

50. HOUSEHOLDERS

1. Whose home was used as a prison for Jeremiah?
2. What tanner lived in a seaside house?
3. Who lived next door to a synagogue?
4. What did Abraham use for a home?
5. Who stored the ark in his house for three months?
6. What king owned a house made of ivory?
7. Who lived in a house built of cedar?
8. Whose home was used for prayer meetings?
9. Who added a guest chamber on the roof of their house to accommodate a prophet?
10. What family clansmen were prohibited by their father from building houses?

51. HOSPITABLE PEOPLE

1. What girl was hospitable to a stranger, giving him a drink of water and watering his camels?

2. What priest with seven daughters welcomed a stranger who had appeared at a well?

3. What man in the island of Melita showed hospitality to shipwrecked strangers?

4. Who welcomed three strangers, inviting them to rest in the shade of a tree?

5. Who was told to go to Zarephath to receive a hospitable welcome from a widow?

6. Who said, "The stranger did not lodge in the street, but I opened my door to the traveller"?

7. Who welcomed two angels, inviting them to wash their feet and spend the night?

8. Who showed hospitality to a man because of a former friendship with the man's father?

9. What prominent woman showed hospitality to a prophet who stopped in at her home from time to time?

10. What man living in a rented house welcomed all who visited him?

52. HUSBANDS

1. What husband had a wife who was turned into a pillar of salt?

2. What husband had a wife who said to him, "Dost thou still retain thine integrity? Curse God and die"?

3. What husband asked his wife, "Am I not better to thee than ten sons"?

4. What husband had a wife who disapproved of his dancing in the street?

5. What husband was sent to war to be killed because another man coveted his wife?

6. What two husbands lied, saying their wives were their sisters?

7. What husband was exiled because of a disobedient wife?

8. What royal husband banished his wife because she disobeyed him?

9. What husband had 700 wives?

10. Who worked seven years to earn his wife?

53. IDOLATORS

1. Who made molten images for Baal and burned incense under every green tree?

2. What sinful king set up two golden calves as idols?

3. Who placed a great golden image on a plain and commanded his subjects to fall down and worship it?

4. What king was drawn to idolatry by his wives?

5. What king rebuilt the heathen altars his father had broken down and encouraged his subjects to worship idols?

6. What king, after marrying a wicked queen, began the worship of Baal and built a temple and altar to Baal in Samaria?

7. What queen was removed from her throne because she had made an idol in a grove?

8. Who took earrings and made them into a golden calf for them to worship?

9. What king died a leper because he insisted on burning incense at the altar?

10. Who had an idol made from silver shekels her son had stolen from her and then returned?

54. INJURED PEOPLE

Fill in each blank with the name of an injured person who is described in the accompanying clue.

1. _____ was permanently crippled from childhood, after being dropped by his nurse.

2. _____ had his hip dislocated during a wrestling match with an angel.

3. _____ had his ear cut off by Peter.

4. _____ fell backwards from a seat by a gate and broke his neck.

5. _____ had his eyes put out by the Babylonian enemy.

6. _____ fell from an upper window and was seriously injured.

7. _____ had his foot crushed against a wall by a mule.

8. _____ had his skull crushed by a piece of millstone thrown by a woman.

9. _____ shook his fist at a prophet, and his arm became paralyzed in that position.

10. _____ cried out, "All my bones are out of joint."

55. IN-LAWS

1. Who gave good advice to his son-in-law?

2. Who was an unusually devoted daughter-in-law?

3. Who felt he was unworthy to become a king's son-in-law?

4. What father-in-law was given warning by God in a dream not to speak harshly to his son-in-law?

5. Whose mother-in-law was healed by Jesus?

6. What was the name of Naomi's daughter-in-law who did not take the trip back to Bethlehem?

7. Who had his wages changed ten times by his father-in-law?

8. What former slave became the son-in-law of a powerful priest of On?

9. Who burned Philistine grain, and the Philistines then burned his father-in-law?

10. Who was invited by his brother-in-law to go on a long journey?

56. JEALOUS PEOPLE

Some Scripture folk were miserably jealous. See if you can match these persons, listed in the left-hand column, with the persons they were jealous of.

1. Saul	a. Mordecai
2. Philistines	b. Moses
3. Rachel	c. Jesus
4. Laban's Sons	d. Isaac
5. Cain	e. Hagar
6. Miriam	f. David
7. Sarah	g. Joseph
8. Chief Priests	h. Jacob
9. Jacob's Sons	i. Leah
10. Haman	j. Abel

57. JUDGES

In the left-hand column are the scrambled names of some people who served when Israel was ruled by judges. After you have unscrambled the names, match each one to the event or deed that identifies the person.

1. AMECEHIBL   a. Lost his strength when his hair was cut.

2. BADEHOR   b. Captured a town and won a bride.

3. AAMSRHG   c. Hit on the head by a millstone, thrown by a woman.

4. HDEU   d. Sacrificed his daughter because of a vow.

5. EINOGD   e. Lived under a palm tree.

6. AELMSU   f. Left-handed murderer.

7. OHTEINL   g. Killed 600 Philistines with an ox-goad.

8. LIE   h. Made his two sons judges.

9. HEJATHPH   i. Tested God with a fleece.

10. NAMOSS   j. Fell from a seat and broke his neck.

58. KIND PEOPLE

Fill in each blank with the name of a person(s) who performed the kind act described in the accompanying clue.

1. _____ showed kindness to a new gleaner.
2. _____ provided for the poor by not reaping field corners.
3. _____ cared for a wounded traveler.
4. _____ fed shipwrecked men for three days.
5. _____ was kind to an imprisoned missionary.
6. _____ gave water to a traveler and his camels.
7. _____ arranged for a lame man to always eat at his table.
8. _____ made coats and garments for the needy.
9. _____ brought supplies to a fugitive.
10. _____ kept a room ready for a prophet's use.

59. KINFOLK

In this gathering of Scripture kinfolk, see how many family ties you can identify.

WHAT RELATION IS:

1. Andrew to Peter
2. Othniel to Achsah
3. Mary to Elizabeth
4. Jethro to Moses
5. Hannah to Samuel
6. Lois to Timothy
7. Laban to Jacob
8. Bathsheba to Eliam
9. Lot to Abraham
10. Methuselah to Noah

60. KINGS

Match each king to his description.

1. Asa	a. Was cut in pieces by a prophet.
2. Saul	b. Had a huge iron bed.
3. Hezekiah	c. Ate grass like oxen.
4. Jehoiakim	d. Had 4,000 stalls for his chariots and horses.
5. Solomon	e. Tore a prophet's robe.
6. Nebuchadnezzar	f. Was granted an extension on his life.
7. Agag	g. Cut up a book and burned it.
8. David	h. Saw handwriting on a wall.
9. Og	i. Suffered with a foot disease.
10. Belshazzar	j. Had a national census taken of his subjects.

61. LIARS

1. Who lied about the sale of property?
2. What two men, at separate times, lied about their wives?
3. Who lied about the presence of spies?
4. What greedy servant lied to get money and clothing?
5. Who lied about his acquaintance with Jesus?
6. Who lied, denying a laugh of disbelief?
7. So that he might obtain provisions, who lied to a priest, pretending he had been sent from a king?
8. Who lied to cover up the murder of a brother?
9. Who told a series of three lies to a woman?
10. Who, by lying to his father, obtained his brother's blessing?

62. LEADERS

1. After Moses' death who became the new leader of the Israelites?

2. What imprisoned religious leader was released from jail by an angel?

3. What fugitive, while hiding in a cave, became the leader of hundreds of rebels?

4. Who refused to lead men into battle unless accompanied by a woman?

5. Who led a group of frightened men to Jerusalem?

6. What leader had problems with his followers?

7. After murdering a king, who blew a trumpet, mustered an army, and led them against enemy Moabites?

8. What leader obtained permission to escort a second colony of Jews to Jerusalem?

9. What military leader refused to be made king?

10. What ambitious person did John mention as wanting to push himself forward as the leader of the Christians?

63. MEN OF WAR

1. What military leader was persuaded by a woman to take the head of one man rather than attack an entire city?

2. What military leader commanded the sun and moon to stand still?

3. What military leader won a battle by having his men blow trumpets and break jars?

4. After taking a city, what military leader covered the ground with salt?

5. What military leader refused to lead a battle unless accompanied by a woman?

6. What captain, escaping a battle, took refuge in a woman's tent?

7. What left-handed man, after assassinating a king, led a battle in which 10,000 Moabites were killed?

8. Which of David's top three mighty men fought a successful battle in the middle of a barley field?

9. What general made a vow that if he were victorious in battle, he would offer as a sacrifice whoever was first from his house to greet him?

10. What military man captured a city, and as a reward was given a bride?

64. MESSENGERS

1. What man, pretending to be a messenger from God, murdered a king?

2. Who sent messengers to arrange a meeting with an estranged brother?

3. Who sent messengers to a king, asking permission for a company of people to pass through his country?

4. What king, injured by a fall, sent messengers to the god Baalzebub, asking if he would recover?

5. What prophet sent a messenger to a leprous man, telling him to wash seven times in the river Jordan?

6. Who sent messengers to a man's tent to look for stolen property?

7. Who said a messenger of Satan was sent to "buffet" him?

8. What king sent out messengers to find a harpist?

9. What prophet offered to be a messenger for God, saying, "Here am I; send me"?

10. Who sent out messengers with letters, decreeing that all Jews were to be destroyed?

65. MIRACLE WORKERS

Listed at the left are ten miracle workers. In the right-hand column their outstanding deeds are described. See if you can match them.

1. Moses		a.	Healed a lame man
2. Jesus		b.	Made a sun dial's shadow go backward ten degrees
3. Elijah		c.	Made an iron axehead float on water
4. Samson		d.	Turned water into wine
5. Peter		e.	Made the sun and moon stand still
6. Elisha		f.	Got water from a rock
7. Isaiah		g.	Killed 1,000 men with the jawbone of an ass
8. Paul		h.	Changed a rod into a serpent
9. Joshua		i.	Restored life to a man who had fallen from a high window
10. Aaron		j.	Brought fire twice from heaven to destroy captains and their men

66. MOTHERS

1. Who was the "mother of all living"?
2. What mother "lent her child to the Lord"?
3. What mother urged her daughter to ask for a man's head?
4. What mother asked Jesus if her two sons could sit on His right and left hand in His kingdom?
5. What mother helped her son deceive his father?
6. What mother served as a paid nurse for her baby son?
7. What 90-year-old woman became a mother?
8. What mother arranged for her son to marry an Egyptian girl?

67. MURDERERS

1. Who was the first murderer mentioned in the Bible?
2. What left-handed man murdered a fat king?
3. What grandmother murdered all her grandchildren, except one little boy?
4. What two men murdered a man as he took a noontime nap?
5. Who murdered a man who refused to stop chasing him?
6. What woman gave a man a drink of milk and then murdered him?
7. Who put a wet blanket on a king's face, smothering him to death?
8. Who became a fugitive because he murdered a cruel Egyptian?
9. Who murdered a half-drunk king and then killed the entire royal family?
10. Who attempted murder with a javelin?

68. MUSICIANS

1. Who made a sound with cymbals?
2. What prophetess played the timbrel?
3. What king organized Levites at the temple into an orchestral group?
4. Who invented the harp and organ?
5. Who was a skillful harp player?
6. Who said, "I am become as sounding brass, or a tinkling cymbal"?
7. Who hung their harps "upon the willows"?
8. How many Levites did David appoint to furnish instrumental music for temple worship?
9. At the anointing of which king did the people "pipe with pipes"?
10. On what occasion did David and "all the house of Israel play before the Lord on all manner of instruments . . . even on harps, and on psalteries, and on timbrels, and on cornets and on cymbals"?

69. NAMELESS PEOPLE

Often people mentioned in the Bible were not named. Some of these nameless persons are listed at the left. Match them with the event in which they participated.

1. Woman of Samaria
2. Lot's Wife
3. Good Samaritan
4. Ethiopian Woman
5. Pharaoh's Daughter
6. Jephthah's Daughter
7. Shunammite Woman
8. Ethiopian Eunuch
9. Prodigal Son
10. Herodias' Daughter

a. Disliked by her husband's family
b. Converted by Philip
c. Asked for a man's head
d. Repented of foolish living
e. Elisha's hostess
f. Met Jesus at a well
g. Sacrificed because of a vow
h. Found a baby named Moses
i. Turned into a pillar of salt
j. Helped a traveler attacked by bandits

70. OBEDIENT PEOPLE

The people listed at the left were rewarded in various ways for their obedience to God. Their rewards are listed at the right. See if you can match them.

1. Elijah
2. Abram
3. Caleb
4. Noah

a. Buried among kings
b. Deliverance from enemies
c. Fed by ravens
d. Could build fortified cities, for his land was at peace

5. Joshua
6. Hezekiah
7. Jehoshaphat
8. Jehoiada

e. Riches and honor
f. Conquered an entire land
g. Saved from a watery disaster
h. Descendants multiplied like stars in the sky

9. David
10. Asa

i. Prospered in everything he did
j. Possession of land

71. PRAYING PEOPLE

Fill in each blank with the name of the person who made the accompanying petition.

1. _____ prayed for a drought
2. _____ prayed for victory over an enemy
3. _____ prayed for a drink of water
4. _____ prayed for a blessing on his house
5. _____ prayed for a son
6. _____ prayed for the healing of a leprosy case
7. _____ prayed for protection from a brother
8. _____ prayed to be returned to Jerusalem and his kingdom
9. _____ prayed for the blinding of an army
10. _____ prayed for guidance in bringing up a child

72. POOR PEOPLE

Match each poor person in the left-hand column to the unprosperous circumstance listed at the right.

1. David
2. Lazarus
3. Gideon
4. Prophet's Widow
5. Israelites
6. Job
7. Widow of Zarephath
8. Prodigal Son
9. Macedonians
10. Widow of Jerusalem

a. Even though poverty-stricken, gave money to a cause

b. Told God his family was the poorest in the tribe of Manasseh

c. "When he had spent all, there arose a mighty famine in that land; and he began to be in want"

d. Lay at a rich man's gate, hoping to be fed with crumbs

e. Felt he was unworthy to be a king's son-in-law because he was poor

f. Had only a small amount of food to eat

g. Had to mortgage property, borrow money, and lose children to bondage

h. Put two tiny coins in a treasury

i. After losing all his wealth, he said, "The Lord gave, and the Lord hath taken away"

j. Was going to lose her sons to creditor because of debt

73. PREACHERS

1. Who preached so long that one of his listeners fell asleep and tumbled from a high window to his death?

2. Which book of the Bible includes the word *Preacher* in its subtitle?

3. Whose preaching caused the king of Nineveh to step down from his throne, put on sackcloth, and sit in ashes?

4. What prophet said, "The Lord hath anointed me to preach good tidings"?

5. Who received instructions to preach "upon the house tops"?

6. Who preached in the wilderness of Judaea?

7. Who so angered people with his preaching that they tried to push him over a cliff?

8. Whose preaching on the day of Pentecost resulted in about 3,000 people being converted and baptized?

9. What early Bible person did Peter call a "preacher of righteousness"?

10. Whose preaching brought about the conversion of Simon the sorcerer?

74. PRIESTS

Fill in each blank with the name of a priest who fits the accompanying description.

1. _____ was Joseph's father-in-law
2. _____ bored a hole in the lid of a chest and used it to hold money contributions
3. _____ succeeded Aaron as high priest
4. _____ returned to Jerusalem with his countrymen
5. _____ had wicked sons
6. _____ gave David shewbread and Goliath's sword
7. _____ was the only priest to escape Doeg's slaughter of priests
8. _____ was instructed to make an altar, copying one seen by Ahaz
9. _____ became the first high priest of Israel
10. _____ was involved in a plot to destroy Jesus

75. PRISONERS

1. Who was the prisoner released instead of Jesus?
2. What two men were in prison when an earthquake opened its doors?
3. Who was rescued by an Ethiopian eunuch from a cistern where he was imprisoned?
4. How many days did Joseph keep his brothers in prison?
5. What king, after spending thirty-seven years in prison, was released by another king?
6. What blinded prisoner was made to grind grain in jail?
7. Who was rescued from prison by an angel?
8. Who was brought from a dungeon to interpret a king's dream?
9. Who was imprisoned at the demand of a king's wife?

76. PROPHETS

Fill in each blank with the name of the prophet who fits the accompanying description.

1. _____ was suspended between heaven and earth by a lock of his hair

2. _____ saw horses of different colors on mountains of brass

3. _____ wrote the shortest book in the Old Testament

4. _____ was mocked by children because of his bald head

5. _____ cultivated sycamore trees

6. _____ was put in stocks

7. _____ had a remedy for boils

8. _____ spent three days and nights inside a fish

9. _____ was swept up to heaven by a whirlwind

10. _____ spent a night in a lions' den

77. QUEENS

Match these queens to their descriptions.

1. Jezebel   a. A throne was ordered for her so she could sit by her royal son

2. Candace   b. An orphan girl who became queen

3. Jeroboam's Wife   c. Vowed to kill Elijah

4. Bernice   d. Banished by a king for not exhibiting herself at a banquet

5. Athaliah   e. Queen of the Ethiopians

6. Queen of Sheba   f. "With great pomp" entered the courtroom where Paul was being tried

7. Esther   g. Went in disguise to visit a prophet

8. Maachah   h. Gave an intelligence test to a king

9. Vashti   i. Killed all her grandchildren except one little boy

10. Bathsheba   j. Was removed from being queen because she made an idol in a grove

78. RUNNERS

1. Who said, "Know ye not that they which run in a race run all, but one receiveth the prize? So run, that ye may obtain"?
2. Who ran to a tent to tell his wife to make a meal for visitors?
3. What woman ran to report a missing body?
4. What two men ran to bring news to David?
5. Who could run like a deer?
6. What preacher ran to speak to a man who was reading in a chariot?
7. Who ran ahead of a crowd and climbed a tree to get a look at Jesus?
8. What child ran to a priest in the night, thinking he had called?
9. Who ran to get water for camels?
10. Who ran to greet an estranged brother?

79. SCRIBES

1. David's uncle was a "counsellor, a wise man, and a scribe." What was his name?
2. What scribe was sent by King Hezekiah with a message to Isaiah?
3. Who denounced scribes?
4. What scribe wrote to King Artaxerxes, opposing the rebuilding of Jerusalem?
5. To what scribe did Hilkiah give a scroll to read?
6. What scribe did Nehemiah appoint as treasurer of Jerusalem's storehouses?
7. What scribe kept the muster roll of Uzziah's host of fighting men?
8. To what scribe did Jeremiah dictate his prophecy?
9. What scribe read the book of Moses' law from a wooden pulpit?
10. Who called in a king's scribes and dictated letters to them to be sent throughout the kingdom?

80. SERVANTS

1. What servant was sent to find a wife for his master's son?

2. What servant of King Saul killed eighty-five priests?

3. What servant of a high priest had his ear cut off by Simon Peter?

4. What maid servant was cruelly treated by a jealous mistress?

5. What covetous servant lied to his master about money?

6. What servant girl answered Peter's knock but was too excited to let him enter?

7. What young slave became a very efficient servant?

8. What servant of Gideon went with him at night to spy on the Midianite camp?

9. What servant of Saul had fifteen sons and twenty servants?

10. What runaway slave was returned to his former master by Paul?

81. SINGERS

1. What two prisoners sang hymns in prison at midnight?

2. Who sang in front of a golden calf?

3. What king wrote 1,005 songs?

4. Where did the disciples go after they had sung a hymn?

5. What king who was slain in battle was mourned in song by temple choirs?

6. What two people sang a victory song?

7. What king had a singing choir lead the march into battle?

8. Who sang a song that mentioned God having a horse and rider thrown into the sea?

9. How were singers chosen for their term of service in the tabernacle?

82. SOLDIERS

1. What Roman soldier was converted by Paul?

2. What woman helped command 10,000 soldiers?

3. Which of David's soldiers saved him from being killed by a giant?

4. What drink did soldiers offer Jesus while He was on the cross?

5. Paul was in the custody of what soldier when they encountered a storm at sea?

6. On David's orders what soldier was sent to the front lines so he would be killed?

7. What brother, serving as a soldier, scolded a younger brother for coming to the battlefield?

8. According to the Israelite law, how long was a newly-married man exempt from being drafted into the army?

9. What king's son and his armor-bearer showed great bravery in attacking an enemy garrison?

10. What soldier was with David at Pas-dammim and killed Philistines in a barley field?

83. SONS

Match the sons listed in the left column to their descriptions listed on the right.

1. Jonathan
2. Esau
3. Timothy
4. Absalom
5. Jacob
6. Asa
7. Moses
8. Enoch
9. Prodigal Son
10. Joseph

a. Fell into his father's arms and wept a long time

b. Was the adopted son of a princess

c. Became so angry with his father he left the table without eating

d. Said, "I . . . am no more worthy to be called thy son: make me as one of thy hired servants"

e. Kept his father supplied with venison

f. Conspired against his father

g. Was like a son to Paul

h. Removed his mother from being queen because she made an idol

i. Deceived his father to get his blessing

j. Had a city named after him by his father

84. THIEVES

1. Who confessed to his mother that he had stolen pieces of silver from her?

2. What thief was released instead of Jesus?

3. Who stole household idols from her father?

4. Who stole and hid a wedge of gold, silver, and a Babylonian robe?

5. How many spies robbed Micah of images, ephod, and teraphim?

6. What king of Egypt ransacked the temple and stole the gold shield that Solomon had made?

7. Men of what district set up ambushes on a mountain top and robbed passersby?

8. Which of the disciples was in charge of the disciples' funds and often dipped into them for his own use?

9. Who said, "I robbed other churches, taking wages of them, to do you service"?

10. Who was falsely accused of having stolen a silver cup?

85. TRAVELERS

1. Who insisted on traveling with a prophet, going with him from Bethel to Jericho?

2. Who traveled with a mother-in-law to Bethlehem?

3. Who was a fellow traveler of Saul (Paul) when he set out on his first missionary tour?

4. Who walked alongside two disciples, traveling together to Emmaus?

5. Who traveled to Egypt accompanied by seventy descendants?

6. Who, because of a dream, traveled in the middle of the night with his wife and child?

7. Which uncle and nephew were fellow travelers?

8. What men who were traveling in a group were not allowed to carry food, money, or extra clothing?

9. Who traveled with a servant, enroute to a marriage?

10. How many brothers traveled together to buy grain?

86. UNFAMILIAR PEOPLE

If you are well-informed about the Bible, you'll be able to answer these questions about some of the lesser known Bible people.

1. What was the name of Adam's son who was born after Abel's murder?

2. What was the name of Naomi's daughter-in-law who stayed behind?

3. Jacob had twelve sons, but only one daughter. What was her name?

4. What was the name of Elkanah's second wife, who taunted Hannah for having no children?

5. Who was the man appointed with Bezaleel to beautify the tabernacle?

6. Jael is well known for having killed Sisera. What was her husband's name?

7. What was the name of Saul's daughter who was engaged to David, but had the engagement broken off by her father?

8. What was the name of Abraham's second wife?

9. What was the name of Joash's aunt who rescued him from his wicked grandmother?

10. Ruth's romance and marriage to Boaz is well known, but what was the name of her first husband?

87. WATCHERS

1. Who watched to see what would happen to a hidden baby?

2. Who watched over the slain bodies of two sons through an entire barley season?

3. Who watched Jesus to see if He healed anyone on the Sabbath?

4. What mother watched from a window for her son's chariot?

5. Who watched the lips of a praying woman?

6. Who said, "I watch, and am as a sparrow alone upon the house top"?

7. Among the women watching Jesus' crucifixion, who were the three whose names were mentioned?

8. What prophet was told by God, "Go, set a watchman, let him declare what he seeth"?

9. What three disciples were unable to keep watch with Jesus in Gethsemane because of sleepiness?

10. When Jerusalem's walls were rebuilt, who set up citizens as watchmen over the city and their homes?

88. WEEPERS

1. What barefooted man wept as he climbed Mount Olivet?

2. Who kissed a girl he just met and then wept?

3. What dying king had his life prolonged for fifteen years because God saw him weeping?

4. Who wept bitterly when he heard a cock crow?

5. Who was surrounded by weeping friends just before he boarded a ship?

6. Who wept at the sight of Jerusalem?

7. What prophet was forbidden by God to weep when his wife died?

8. What king wept when he learned an enemy had spared his life?

9. What childless woman cried so much she was unable to eat?

89. WEALTHY PEOPLE

Match the names of these wealthy people of Scripture times with their descriptions.

1. Isaac

a. He became so wealthy he had to construct special treasury buildings to hold his riches.

2. Jehoshaphat

b. He "exceeded all the kings of the earth for riches."

3. Nabal

c. He was told to dispose of his wealth and give to the poor.

4. Rich young ruler

d. His wealth came from tax collecting.

5. Job

e. He was the first man mentioned in the Bible as being very rich.

6. Hezekiah

f. He held a six-month celebration to display his wealth.

7. Abram

g. His willing subjects paid him so many taxes he became very wealthy.

8. Solomon

h. Although wealthy, he was stingy and rude.

9. Zacchaeus

i. He lost his wealth, then regained it.

10. Ahasuerus

j. His wealth made the Philistines so jealous they destroyed his wells.

90. WIVES

Match each wife to her description.

1. Vashti   a. She was given to her husband as a reward for conquering a city

2. Jezebel   b. Traveled a long way by camel to marry a man she had never seen

3. Michal   c. Refused to display her beauty to her husband's banquet guests

4. Abigail   d. Was the first wife to get her husband in trouble

5. Zeresh   e. Joined her husband in a lie about selling property

6. Sarah   f. Told her husband to make a gallows

7. Sapphira   g. Disobeyed her husband and supplied a man and his soldiers with provisions

8. Achsah   h. Arranged to get her husband a vineyard

9. Rebekah   i. Pretended to be her husband's sister

10. Eve   j. Saved her husband's life by letting him down through a window

ANSWERS

1. ACCUSERS

1. Joseph (Gen. 42:8, 9)
2. Saul (I Sam. 22:7, 8)
3. Asian Jews (Acts 21:27, 28)
4. They were thrown into a lion's den (Dan. 6:1-24)
5. Unjust steward (Luke 16:1, 2)
6. Demetrius (Acts 19:24-27)
7. Irijah (Jer. 37:12-14)
8. Korah (Num. 16:1-5)
9. Pharisees (Matt. 12:1, 2)
10. Jezebel (I Kings 21:6-10)

2. ANGRY PEOPLE

1. Moses (Exod. 11:8)
2. Eliab (I Sam. 17:28)
3. Saul (I Sam. 11:4-7)
4. Nebuchadnezzar (Dan. 3:19, 20)
5. Cain (Gen. 4:4-6)
6. Balaam (Num. 22:27)
7. Ahasuerus (Esther 7:7)
8. Jonathan (I Sam. 20:34)

3. AUTHORS

1. Moses (Exod. 17:14)
2. John (Rev. 1:10, 11)
3. Jesus (Luke 4:16, 17)
4. David (Ps. 45:1)
5. Jeremiah (Jer. 51:60-63)
6. Job (Job 19:23)
7. Solomon (I Kings 4:32)
8. Samuel (I Sam. 10:25)
9. Obadiah
10. Nathan (II Chron. 9:29)

4. BABIES

1. Moses (Exod. 2:10)
2. Isaac (Gen. 21:8)
3. Moses (Exod. 2:7-9)
4. Obed (Ruth 4:15-17)
5. Jacob (Gen. 25:24-26)
6. Benjamin (Gen. 35:18)
7. Job (Job 3:11)
8. Cain (Gen. 4:1)
9. Jesus (Luke 2:8-12)
10. John (Luke 1:13, 60)

5. BEAUTIFUL PEOPLE

1. Ahasuerus (Esther 1:3, 10, 11)
2. Absalom (II Sam. 14:25)
3. David (I Sam. 16:11, 12)
4. Job (Job 42:15)
5. Esther (Esther 2:2-17)
6. Rebekah (Gen. 24:16-18)
7. Saul (I Sam. 9:2)
8. Bathsheba (II Sam. 11:1-3)
9. Joseph (Gen. 39:1, 6)
10. Rachel (Gen. 29:17, 18)

6. BEREAVED PEOPLE

1. Aaron (Lev. 10:1, 2, 6)
2. Naomi (Ruth 1:1-5, 20)
3. Ezekiel (Ezek. 24:15-18)
4. Joseph (Gen. 50:4-6)
5. Abraham (Gen. 23:1-6)
6. Job (Job 1:1, 2, 18-20)
7. David (II Sam. 18:33)
8. Jairus (Luke 8:41-50)
9. Jacob (Gen. 35:19, 20)
10. Rizpah (II Sam. 21:8-10)

7. BLESSERS

1. g (Gen. 27:27, 30)
2. d (Josh. 14:13)
3. h (Gen. 31:55)
4. j (Gen. 14:18, 19)
5. i (II Sam. 19:39)
6. c (Deut. 33:1)
7. a (Luke 2:33, 34)
8. b (I Sam. 2:20)
9. f (Gen. 47:7)
10. e (Judg. 5:1, 24)

8. BLIND PEOPLE

1. (a) Nahash (I Sam. 11:1, 2)
2. (c) Ahijah (I Kings 14:2-4)
3. (c) Elisha (II Kings 6:18)
4. (a) Elymas (Acts 13:8-11)
5. (b) Lot (Gen. 19:1-11)
6. (c) Isaac (Gen. 27)
7. (a) Zedekiah (II Kings 25:5-7)
8. (c) Bartimaeus (Mark 10:46-52)
9. (b) Paul (Acts 9:8-20)
10. (a) Samson (Judg. 16:21-30)

9. BOYS

1. Mephibosheth (II Sam. 4:4)
2. Enoch (Gen. 4:17)
3. Isaac (Gen. 22:6-8)
4. Jesus (Luke 2:42-47)
5. Joseph (Gen. 37:2, 3)
6. Ephraim & Manasseh (Gen. 48:1-10)
7. Samuel (I Sam. 2:18, 19)
8. Joash (II Chron. 24:1)
9. Shunammite's Son (II Kings 4:1, 18-35)
10. Ishmael (Gen. 21:9-19)

10. BROTHERS

1. f (I Kings 2:22-25)
2. d (Lev. 10:1, 2)
3. i (Gen. 4:25)
4. h (Exod. 4:14-15)
5. j (Matt. 4:18)
6. b (Gen. 27:41)
7. e (I Sam. 17:28)
8. c (Matt. 4:21, 22)
9. g (Judg. 1:3)
10. a (Gen. 43:29-34)

11. BUILDERS

1. Omri (I Kings 16:23, 24)
2. Jacob (Gen. 33:17)
3. Uzziah (II Chron. 26:9)
4. Paul (I Cor. 3:10)
5. Bezaleel (Exod. 35:30-35; 37:1; 38:1-7)
6. Jotham (II Chron. 27:1, 4)
7. Noah (Gen. 6:14-16)
8. Hezekiah (II Chron. 32:30)
9. Cain (Gen. 4:17)
10. Nehemiah (Neh. 4:15-18)

12. BUSINESS PEOPLE

1. Joseph (Gen. 41:54-57)
2. Paul (Acts 18:1-3)
3. Elisha (II Kings 4:2-7)
4. Lydia (Acts 16:14)
5. Jehoshaphat & Ahaziah (II Chron. 20:35, 36)
6. Demetrius (Acts 19:24-27)
7. Ezekiel (Ezek. 27)
8. Levi (Luke 5:27, 28)
9. Hiram (I Chron. 14:1; II Chron. 2:11, 16)
10. Solomon (I Kings 10:28)

13. BUYERS

1. e   (Gen. 39:1)
2. a   (Gen. 23:13-19)
3. g   (II Sam. 24:24)
4. b   (Gen. 47:20)
5. j   (Matt. 27:6, 7)
6. c   (Ruth 4:10)
7. d   (Mark 15:43, 46)
8. f   (Gen. 33:18, 19)
9. h   (I Kings 16:23, 24)
10. i   (Mark 16:1)

14. CAPTAINS

1. Naaman (II Kings 5:1)
2. Adino (II Sam. 23:8)
3. Sisera (Judg. 4:2, 18, 21)
4. Abner (I Sam. 14:50)
5. Claudius Lysias (Acts 23:18, 26, 27)
6. Potiphar (Gen. 37:36)
7. Jephthah (Judg. 11:1, 5, 6)
8. David (I Sam. 22:1, 2)
9. Amasa (II Sam. 19:13)
10. Nebuzar-adan (II Kings 25:8, 9)

15. CAPTIVES

1. Lot (Gen. 14:9-16)
2. Jehoiachin (II Kings 25:27-30)
3. Ezekiel (Ezek. 1:1)
4. Joseph (Gen. 41:1-41)
5. Daniel (Dan. 1:3-6)
6. Zedekiah (Jer. 52:9-11)
7. Jews (Ps. 137:2, 3)
8. Jehoiachin (II Kings 24:11-16)
9. Ezra
10. Mordecai (Esther 2:5; 8:1, 2, 15)

16. CATTLEMEN

1. Elisha (I Kings 19:19)
2. Obadiah & Ahab (I Kings 18:5, 6)
3. Job (Job 1:3, 14, 15)
4. Jacob (Gen. 33:17)
5. Abraham & Lot (Gen. 13:1-9)
6. Amos (Amos 1:1)
7. Isaac (Gen. 26:12-15)
8. Laban (Gen. 30:27-30)
9. Doeg the Edomite (I Sam. 21:7)
10. Jabal (Gen. 4:20)

17. CONCEALERS

1. c   (Exod. 2:1-3; 6:20)
2. h   (I Kings 18:4)
3. j   (Jer. 43:9)
4. g   (Gen. 35:2-4)
5. f   (Exod. 2:11, 12)
6. i   (Josh. 2:3-6)
7. e   (Matt. 25:14-18)
8. a   (Josh. 7:20, 21)
9. b   (Gen. 31:19, 34)
10. d   (II Kings 11:2, 3)

18. CONSPIRATORS

1. c   (II Sam. 15:1-12)
2. e   (II Kings 12:20)
3. g   (Judg. 16:4-21)
4. f   (Judg. 9:23-41)
5. i   (Acts 23:12-21)
6. h   (II Kings 9:14-24)
7. b   (Gen. 37:17, 18)
8. j   (I Sam. 22:7-13)
9. d   (Matt. 22:15-18)
10. a   (I Kings 16:8-10)

19. CONVERTS

1. Saul (Paul) (Acts 9:1-20)
2. About 3,000 (Acts 2:41)
3. Cornelius (Acts 10)
4. Philip (Acts 8:26-38)
5. Saul (I Sam. 10:5-7)
6. Simon (Acts 8:9-13)
7. Nebuchadnezzar (Dan. 4)
8. Lydia (Acts 16:14, 15)
9. Simon Peter (Luke 22:31, 32)
10. Sergius Paulus (Acts 13:7-12)

20. COURAGEOUS PEOPLE

1. f (Judg. 7:15-21)
2. d (Num. 16:46-48)
3. i (Dan. 3:10-18)
4. h (II Sam. 23:20, 21)
5. j (Acts 20:22-24)
6. b (Mark 15:43)
7. e (Neh. 6:10-13)
8. c (II Sam. 23:11, 12)
9. g (I Sam. 17:4, 40)
10. a (Dan. 6:6-10)

21. COVENANTERS

1. e (I Kings 5:8-11)
2. d (I Sam. 1:11)
3. b (I Kings 15:18, 19)
4. j (Josh. 2:2-20)
5. g (Gen. 21:30)
6. i (Matt. 26:14, 15)
7. f (I Sam. 18:3, 4)
8. c (I Sam. 11:1, 2)
9. a (Gen. 9:12-16)
10. h (Gen. 31:46-52)

22. COVETOUS PEOPLE

1. Achan (Josh. 7:20, 21)
2. Ahab (I Kings 21:1, 2)
3. Paul (Acts 20:33)
4. Gehazi (II Kings 5:15-24)
5. Balaam (II Peter 2:15)
6. Simon Magus (Acts 8:9, 17-19)
7. Pharisees (Luke 16:14, 15)
8. Felix (Acts 24:25, 26)
9. Eve (Gen. 3:6)
10. Ananias (Acts 5:1, 2)

23. COWARDS

1. j (I Sam. 16:1, 2)
2. g (Gen. 3:11, 12)
3. e (I Sam. 17:21-24)
4. i (Gen. 31:17, 21, 26, 31)
5. b (Matt. 8:26)
6. h (Gen. 12:11-13)
7. c (Luke 22:54-60)
8. d (Judg. 6:25-27)
9. a (Exod. 32:1-5, 22-24)
10. f (John 19:12-16)

24. CRIMINALS

1. j (Judg. 3:16-22)
2. i (Judg. 15:4, 5)
3. f (Josh. 9:3-15)
4. b (Judg. 17:1, 2)
5. g (II Sam. 15:1-6)
6. d (I Sam. 8:1-3)
7. a (Judg. 21:20-23)
8. c (I Kings 21:8)
9. e (Neh. 5:1-13)
10. h (Acts 5:1-3)

25. CRUEL PEOPLE

1. Athaliah (II Kings 11:1-3)
2. Sarah (Gen. 16:6)
3. Herod (Matt. 2:16)
4. Simeon and Levi (Gen. 49:5-7)
5. Pharaoh (Exod. 5:6-18)
6. Nebuchadnezzar (Jer. 52:4, 10, 11)
7. Herodias (Matt. 14:3-10)
8. Rehoboam (I Kings 12:11, 12)
9. Abimelech (Judg. 9:1-5)
10. King of Moab (II Kings 3:26, 27)

26. DAUGHTERS

1. e (I Sam. 18:20)
2. c (I Chron. 3:9)
3. g (Gen. 24:15)
4. a (I Chron. 2:13, 16)
5. h (Gen. 30:19, 21)
6. j (Judg. 1:12)
7. d (Gen. 29:16)
8. i (I Chron. 6:3)
9. b (Exod. 2:18, 21)
10. f (Job 42:14)

27. DECEIVERS

1. David (I Sam. 21:10-15)
2. Gehazi (II Kings 5:20-27)
3. Woman of Tekoa (II Sam. 14:1-19)
4. Jacob (Gen. 27:1-23)
5. Abraham & Isaac (Gen. 12:12, 13; 26:7-10)
6. Ehud (Judg. 3:15-23)
7. Ananias (Acts 5:1-4)
8. Laban (Gen. 29:18-25)
9. Delilah (Judg. 16:5-19)
10. Joseph (Gen. 42:7-17)

28. DISCIPLES

1. Philip (John 1-43)
2. Judas (John 12:4-6; 13:29)
3. Matthew (Matt. 9:9)
4. Didymus (John 21:2)
5. Lebbaeus (Matt. 10:3)
6. Andrew (John 6:8, 9)
7. Peter (Matt. 14:28-31)
8. Nathanael (John 1:47, 48)
9. John (John 19:25-27)
10. James (Acts 12:1, 2)

29. DISEASED PEOPLE

1. c (I Kings 15:23)
2. e (Job 7:3, 4)
3. g (II Kings 5:1)
4. f (I Sam. 25:35-38)
5. i (Luke 16:20)
6. h (II Chron. 21:1, 18)
7. b (Acts 12:21-23)
8. j (Luke 4:38)
9. d (Acts 9:33)
10. a (II Kings 20:1, 7)

30. DISGUISED PEOPLE

1. Saul (I Sam. 28:8)
2. Jeroboam's wife (I Kings 14:2)
3. Gibeonites (Josh. 9:3-6)
4. Jacob (Gen. 27:15-23)
5. Josiah (II Chron. 35:22-24)
6. Ashes on his face (I Kings 20:38)
7. Ahab (II Chron. 18:3, 29)
8. Sheeps' clothing (Matt. 7:15)
9. Joseph (Gen. 42:7)
10. Mourner (II Sam. 14:1-4)

31. DOUBTERS

1. Queen of Sheba (I Kings 10:1, 6, 7)
2. Turn a rod into a serpent (Exod. 4:1-5)
3. Thomas (John 20:24, 25)
4. Zacharias (Luke 1:13-20)
5. Rhoda (Acts 12:12-15)
6. Peter (Matt. 14:29-31)
7. Naaman (II Kings 5:10-12)
8. Jesus (Luke 12:29)

32. DREAMERS

1. Job (Job 7:14)
2. Nebuchadnezzar (Dan. 4:4-11)
3. Gideon (Judg. 7:13)
4. Jacob (Gen. 28:10-12)
5. Eliphaz (Job 4:13-15)
6. Solomon (I Kings 3:5-9)
7. Pharaoh (Gen. 41:17, 18)
8. Joseph (Matt. 2:13, 14)
9. Joseph (Gen. 37:5, 9)
10. Laban (Gen. 31:24)

33. ELDERLY PEOPLE

1. c   (Josh. 14:7-12)
2. e   (I Kings 15:23)
3. g   (Gen. 5:27)
4. f   (II Sam. 19:33-35)
5. i   (Gen. 17:1, 5)
6. h   (I Kings 11:3, 4)
7. b   (Gen. 47:28-31)
8. j   (I Sam. 4:14, 18)
9. d   (Deut. 34:7)
10. a   (I Kings 1:1)

34. ENEMIES

1. Saul (I Sam. 18:28, 29)
2. Haman (Esther 3:10)
3. Sanballat & Tobiah (Neh. 4:1-3)
4. Absalom (II Sam. 15:1-14)
5. Nahash (I Sam. 11:1, 2)
6. Jezebel (I Kings 19:1, 2)
7. Shimei (II Sam. 16:5, 6, 13)
8. Samson (Judg. 16:23, 24)
9. Esau (Gen. 27:41)
10. Daniel (Dan. 6:2-9)

35. ENVIOUS PEOPLE

1. e   (Num. 11:27-29)
2. a   (Esther 5:11-13)
3. g   (Dan. 6:3, 4)
4. b   (Gen. 30:1)
5. j   (I Sam. 18:6-8)
6. c   (Gen. 31:1)
7. d   (Num. 12:1, 2)
8. f   (Mark 15:1, 10)
9. h   (Gen. 4:4, 5)
10. i   (Gen. 26:12-14)

36. ESCAPEES

1. g   (I Sam. 19:12-18)
2. d   (Acts 9:23-25)
3. h   (Gen. 7)
4. j   (II Sam. 17:17-19)
5. i   (Acts 5:18, 19)
6. c   (Exod. 14:29, 30)
7. a   (Jer. 38:7-13)
8. b   (Josh. 2:1-15)
9. f   (I Kings 20:20)
10. e   (Jonah 2:10)

37. EXILES

1. Abram (Gen. 12:1)
2. Hagar (Gen. 21:9-14)
3. Adam (Gen. 3:23, 24)
4. Joseph (Gen. 37:28)
5. Ittai (II Sam. 15:19-21)
6. Cain (Gen. 4:10-14)
7. Jeroboam (I Kings 11:26, 40)
8. Jacob (Gen. 27:42, 43)
9. Cyrus (Ezra 1)
10. Joab (II Sam. 14:1-24)

38. THE FAITHFUL

1. g (Josh. 6:1-16)
2. d (Exod. 14:13-22)
3. h (I Sam. 17:37)
4. j (I Kings 18:19-39)
5. i (II Chron. 14:8-12)
6. c (Gen. 22:1-12)
7. a (Gen. 6:14-22)
8. b (Ezra 8:22, 31)
9. f (Num. 14:6-9)
10. e (Neh. 2:17-20)

39. FARMERS

1. Isaac (Gen. 26:12)
2. Uzziah (II Chron. 26:9, 10)
3. Cain (Gen. 4:2)
4. Jacob (Gen. 33:17)
5. Boaz (Ruth 3:2)
6. Elisha (I Kings 19:19)
7. Gideon (Judg. 6:11)
8. David (I Chron. 27:26-31)
9. Israelites (I Sam. 13:20, 21)
10. Amos (Amos 1:1)

40. FASTERS

1. f (Exod. 34:4, 28)
2. d (I Kings 21:20-27)
3. i (Neh. 1:1-4)
4. h (Matt. 4:1, 2)
5. j (II Sam. 12:15, 16)
6. b (Dan. 6:16-18)
7. e (Ezra (10:2, 6)
8. c (Luke 2:36, 37)
9. g (Dan. 10:1-3)
10. a (Esther 4:15, 16)

41. FATHERS

1. g (Job 42:15)
2. i (Judg. 8:30)
3. b (Gen. 21:5)
4. h (Exod. 2:16, 18)
5. d (Gen. 25:21-24)
6. j (Judg. 10:3, 4)
7. e (Gen. 4:17)
8. a (II Kings 16:2-3)
9. f (Acts 21:8, 9)
10. c (I Sam. 16:8-12)

42. FIRST DOERS

1. g (Gen. 4:17)
2. d (I Sam. 10:17-24)
3. h (Gen. 35:20)
4. j (Gen. 4:21)
5. i (Gen. 23:3, 4, 16-18)
6. c (Gen. 6:14, 22)
7. a (Gen. 10:9)
8. b (Exod. 15)
9. f (Gen. 4:22)
10. e (Gen. 2:15)

43. FRIENDS

1. Onesiphorus (II Tim. 1:16, 17)
2. Eliphaz, Bildad, Zophar (Job 2:11, 13)
3. David & Jonathan (I Sam. 18:1-3)
4. Hushai (II Sam. 16:16-18)
5. Mary, Martha, Lazarus (John 11:5)
6. Herod & Pilate (Luke 23:6-12)
7. Aquila & Priscilla (Rom. 16:3, 4)
8. Hiram (I Kings 5:1; II Sam. 5:11)
9. Abraham (James 2:23)
10. Daniel (Dan. 2:48, 49)

44. FRIGHTENED PEOPLE

1. c   (I Sam. 12:1, 17, 18)
2. e   (Gen. 42:27, 28)
3. g   (I Sam. 18:28, 29)
4. f   (Matt. 17:1, 5-7)
5. i   (Job 4:13-15)
6. h   (Dan. 5:1-6)
7. b   (Matt. 14:29, 30)
8. j   (Dan. 4:4, 5)
9. d   (Exod. 34:29, 30)
10. a   (I Chron. 21:16, 30)

45. FUGITIVES

1. Abiathar (I Sam. 22:17-23)
2. Cain (Gen. 4:8-12)
3. Hagar (Gen. 21:9-14)
4. Jacob (Gen. 27:41-43)
5. Moses (Exod. 2:11-15)
6. Joseph (Matt. 2:13, 14)
7. Absalom (II Sam. 13:28, 38)
8. David (I Sam. 21:10-13)
9. Jeroboam (I Kings 11:40)
10. By the way they pronounced the word 'shibboleth' (Judg. 12:5, 6)

46. GIANTS

1. Goliath (I Sam. 17:4-10; 48-50)
2. Ishbi-benob (II Sam. 21:15-17)
3. Benaiah (I Chron. 11:22, 23)
4. Anaks (Deut. 9:1, 2)
5. Elhanan (I Chron. 20:5)
6. Moses' spies (Num. 13:17, 33)
7. Og (Deut. 3:11)
8. Jonathan, David's nephew (II Sam. 21:20, 21)
9. Benjamin (Josh. 18:11-16)
10. Four (II Sam. 21:16-22)

47. GUESTS

1. Jesus (Luke 10:38-40)
2. Saul (I Sam. 9:19-24)
3. Paul (Acts 28:1, 7)
4. Elisha (II Kings 4:8-10)
5. Benjamin (Gen. 43:31-34)
6. Simon (Luke 7:40-46)
7. Moses (Exod. 2:15-21)
8. Mephibosheth (II Sam. 9:7-10)
9. Abraham's Servant (Gen. 24:23-27)
10. Paul & Silas (Acts 16:14, 15)

48. HEROIC PEOPLE

1. i   (I Sam. 17)
2. e   (Esther 4:8-16)
3. f   (II Sam. 23:13-16)
4. g   (II Sam. 23:11, 12)
5. d   (Judg. 9:50-55)
6. c   (Judg. 7:7-23)
7. a   (Judg. 1:12, 13)
8. j   (Judg. 3:31)
9. b   (Judg. 4:17-21)
10. h   (I Sam. 14:4-14)

49. HELPERS

1. Dorcas (Acts 9:36)
2. Aaron & Hur (Exod. 17:11, 12)
3. Rahab (Josh. 2:1-16)
4. Aquila & Priscilla (Rom. 16:3)
5. Joab (I Chron. 19:8-12)
6. Good Samaritan (Luke 10:30-35)
7. Moses (Exod. 2:15-17)
8. Job (Job 29:12)
9. Simon of Cyrene (Matt. 27:32)
10. Deborah (Judg. 4:4-10)

50. HOUSEHOLDERS

1. Jonathan the scribe (Jer. 37:15)
2. Simon (Acts 10:6)
3. Justus (Acts 18:7)
4. Tent (Gen. 12:7, 8)
5. Obed-edom (I Chron. 13:13, 14)
6. Ahab (I Kings 22:39)
7. David (II Sam. 7:2)
8. Mary, mother of John Mark (Acts 12:12)
9. Shunammite woman & her husband (II Kings 4:8-10)
10. Rechabites (Jer. 35:5, 8, 9)

51. HOSPITABLE PEOPLE

1. Rebekah (Gen. 24:45, 46)
2. Reuel (Exod. 2:16-20)
3. Publius (Acts 27:44; 28:7)
4. Abram (Gen. 18:1-4)
5. Elijah (I Kings 17:8, 9)
6. Job (Job 31:32)
7. Lot (Gen. 19:1, 2)
8. David to Mephibosheth (II Sam. 9:7-13)
9. Shunammite woman (II Kings 4:8-10)
10. Paul (Acts 28:30)

52. HUSBANDS

1. Lot (Gen. 19:15, 26)
2. Job (Job 2:9)
3. Elkanah (I Sam. 1:8)
4. David (II Sam. 6:14, 16)
5. Uriah (II Sam. 11:6-17, 26, 27)
6. Abraham & Isaac (Gen. 12:11-19; 26:7-10)
7. Adam (Gen. 3)
8. Ahasuerus (Esther 1:10-19)
9. Solomon (I Kings 11:3)
10. Jacob (Gen. 29:18, 20)

53. IDOLATORS

1. Ahaz (II Chron. 28:1-4)
2. Jeroboam (I Kings 12:26-30)
3. Nebuchadnezzar (Dan. 3:1-5)
4. Solomon (I Kings 11:4)
5. Manasseh (II Chron. 33:1-3)
6. Ahab (I Kings 16:30-33)
7. Maachah (II Chron. 15:16)
8. Aaron (Exod. 32:2-6)
9. Uzziah (II Chron. 26:16-21)
10. Micah's mother (Judg. 17:1-4)

54. INJURED PEOPLE

1. Mephibosheth (II Sam. 4:4)
2. Jacob (Gen. 32:24, 25)
3. Malchus (John 18:10)
4. Eli (I Sam. 4:16-18)
5. Zedekiah (II Kings 25:5-7)
6. Ahaziah (II Kings 1:2)
7. Balaam (Num. 22:25)
8. Abimelech (II Sam. 11:21)
9. Jeroboam (I Kings 13:1-4)
10. David (Ps. 22:14)

55. IN-LAWS

1. Jethro (Exod. 18:6, 14-24)
2. Ruth (Ruth 1:11-19)
3. David (I Sam. 18:22, 23)
4. Laban (Gen. 31:24)
5. Simon (Mark 1:30, 31)
6. Orpah (Ruth 1:14)
7. Jacob (Gen. 31:7)
8. Joseph (Gen. 41:45-50)
9. Samson (Judg. 15:5, 6)
10. Hobab (Num. 10:29)

56. JEALOUS PEOPLE

1. f (I Sam. 18:6-9)
2. d (Gen. 26:12-14)
3. i (Gen. 30:1)
4. h (Gen. 31:1)
5. j (Gen. 4:4, 5)
6. b (Num. 12:1, 2)
7. e (Gen. 21:9, 10)
8. c (Matt. 27:12, 18)
9. g (Gen. 37:3, 4)
10. a (Esther 5:11-13)

57. JUDGES

1. (c) Abimelech (Judg. 9:53)
2. (e) Deborah (Judg. 4:5)
3. (g) Shamgar (Judg. 3:31)
4. (f) Ehud (Judg. 3:15-21)
5. (i) Gideon (Judg. 6:36-40)
6. (h) Samuel (I Sam. 8:1)
7. (b) Othniel (Judg. 1:12, 13)
8. (j) Eli (I Sam. 4:18)
9. (d) Jephthah (Judg. 11:30-39)
10. (a) Samson (Judg. 16:19, 20)

58. KIND PEOPLE

1. Boaz (Ruth 2:8, 9)
2. Israelites (Lev. 19:1, 2, 10)
3. Good Samaritan (Luke 10:30-35)
4. Publius (Acts 27:44; 28:7)
5. Onesiphorus (II Tim. 1:16)
6. Rebekah (Gen. 24:15-20)
7. David (II Sam. 9:3-7)
8. Dorcas (Acts 9:36, 39)
9. Shobi, Machir, Barzillai (II Sam. 17:27-29)
10. Shunammite woman (II Kings 4:8-10)

59. KINFOLK

1. Brother (Matt. 4:18)
2. Husband (Josh. 15:16, 17)
3. Cousin (Luke 1:36, 38)
4. Father-in-law (Exod. 18:1)
5. Mother (I Sam. 1:20)
6. Grandmother (II Tim. 1:5)
7. Uncle (Gen. 27:42, 43)
8. Daughter (II Sam. 11:3)
9. Nephew (Gen. 12:5)
10. Grandfather (Gen. 5:26-29)

60. KINGS

1. i   (II Chron. 16:12)
2. e   (I Sam. 15:26, 27)
3. f   (II Kings 20:1-6)
4. g   (Jer. 36:1, 21-23)
5. d   (II Chron. 9:25)
6. c   (Dan. 4:33)
7. a   (I Sam. 15:32, 33)
8. j   (II Sam. 24:1, 2)
9. b   (Deut. 3:11)
10. h   (Dan. 5:1, 5)

61. LIARS

1. Ananias & Sapphira (Acts 5:1-4)
2. Abraham & Isaac (Gen. 12:11-19; 20:2; 26:7-10)
3. Rahab (Josh. 2:1-6)
4. Gehazi (II Kings 5:20-27)
5. Peter (Matt. 26:69-74)
6. Sarah (Gen. 18:13-15)
7. David (I Sam. 21:1-3)
8. Cain (Gen. 4:8, 9)
9. Samson (Judg. 16:6-15)
10. Jacob (Gen. 27:10-29)

62. LEADERS

1. Joshua (Josh. 1:1, 2)
2. Peter (Acts 12:3-11)
3. David (I Sam. 22:1, 2)
4. Barak (Judg. 4:5-9)
5. Jesus (Mark 10:32)
6. Moses (Num. 20:3-5)
7. Ehud (Judg. 3:16-28)
8. Ezra (Ezra 7)
9. Gideon (Judg. 8:22, 23)
10. Diotrephes (III John 9)

63. MEN OF WAR

1. Joab (II Sam. 20:15-22)
2. Joshua (Josh. 10:12, 13)
3. Gideon (Judg. 7:15-22)
4. Abimelech (Judg. 9:45)
5. Barak (Judg. 4:5-8)
6. Sisera (Judg. 4:15-21)
7. Ehud (Judg. 3:21-29)
8. Eleazar (I Chron. 11:12-14)
9. Jephthah (Judg. 11:30-34)
10. Othniel (Judg. 1:12, 13)

64. MESSENGERS

1. Ehud (Judg. 3:20-22)
2. Jacob (Gen. 32:3-6)
3. Moses (Num. 20:14-17)
4. Ahaziah (II Kings 1:2)
5. Elisha (II Kings 5:9, 10)
6. Joshua (Josh. 7:21, 22)
7. Paul (II Cor. 12:7)
8. Saul (I Sam. 16:14-19)
9. Isaiah (Isa. 6:8)
10. Haman (Esther 3:12, 13)

65. MIRACLE WORKERS

1. f (Num. 20:7-11)
2. d (John 2:1-11)
3. j (II Kings 1:9-12)
4. g (Judg. 15:14-16)
5. a (Acts 3:2-8)
6. c (II Kings 6:5, 6)
7. b (II Kings 20:8-11)
8. i (Acts 20:9-12)
9. e (Josh. 10:12, 13)
10. h (Exod. 7:10)

66. MOTHERS

1. Eve (Gen. 3:20)
2. Hannah (I Sam. 1:22, 28)
3. Herodias (Matt. 14:6-8)
4. Zebedee's Wife (Matt. 20:20, 21)
5. Rebekah (Gen. 27:6-19)
6. Jochebed (Exod. 2:1-9; 6:20)
7. Sarah (Gen. 17:15-17)
8. Hagar (Gen. 21:17, 21)

67. MURDERERS

1. Cain (Gen. 4:8)
2. Ehud (Judg. 3:15-22)
3. Athaliah (II Kings, 11:1-3)
4. Rechab & Baanah (II Sam. 4:5-7)
5. Abner (II Sam. 2:18-23)
6. Jael (Judg. 5:24-27)
7. Hazael (II Kings 8:9-15)
8. Moses (Exod. 2:11-15)
9. Zimri (I Kings 16:9, 10)
10. Saul (I Sam. 19:10)

68. MUSICIANS

1. Asaph (I Chron. 16:5)
2. Miriam (Exod. 15:20)
3. Hezekiah (II Chron. 29:20, 25)
4. Jubal (Gen. 4:21)
5. David (I Sam. 16:16, 23)
6. Paul (I Cor. 13:1)
7. Captive Jews (Ps. 137:2, 3)
8. Four thousand (I Chron. 23:4, 5)
9. Solomon (I Kings 1:39, 40)
10. When the ark was brought out of Abinadab's house (II Sam. 6:2, 5)

69. NAMELESS PEOPLE

1. f   (John 4:6, 7)
2. i   (Gen. 19:23-26)
3. j   (Luke 10:30-35)
4. a   (Num. 12:1)
5. h   (Exod. 2:5, 6)
6. g   (Judg. 11:30-39)
7. e   (II Kings 4:8-10)
8. b   (Acts 8:27-38)
9. d   (Luke 15:11-19)
10. c   (Matt. 14:6-8)

70. OBEDIENT PEOPLE

1. c   (I Kings 17:1-6)
2. h   (Gen. 22:16-18)
3. j   (Num. 14:24)
4. g   (Gen. 6–7)
5. f   (Josh. 11:15, 16)
6. i   (II Kings 18:1, 5-7)
7. e   (II Chron. 17:3-5)
8. a   (II Chron. 24:15, 16)
9. b   (II Sam. 22:18-23)
10. d   (II Chron. 14:1-7)

71. PRAYING PEOPLE

1. Elijah or Elias (James 5:17, 18)
2. Asa (II Chron. 14:8-11)
3. Samson (Judg. 15:18, 19)
4. David (II Sam. 7:29)
5. Hannah (I Sam. 1:10, 11)
6. Moses (Num. 12:10, 13)
7. Jacob (Gen. 32:9-11)
8. Manasseh (II Chron. 33:11-13)
9. Elisha (II Kings 6:18)
10. Manoah (Judg. 13:8)

72. POOR PEOPLE

1. e   (I Sam. 18:22, 23)
2. d   (Luke 16:20, 21)
3. b   (Judg. 6:15)
4. j   (II Kings 4:1-7)
5. g   (Neh. 5:1-5)
6. i   (Job 1:14-21)
7. f   (I Kings 17:12)
8. c   (Luke 15:14)
9. a   (II Cor. 8:1-5)
10. h   (Mark 12:42-44)

73. PREACHERS

1. Paul (Acts 20:7-9)
2. Ecclesiastes
3. Jonah (Jonah 3:2-6)
4. Isaiah (Isa. 61:1)
5. 12 apostles (Matt. 10:27)
6. John the Baptist (Matt. 3:1)
7. Jesus (Luke 4:18-29)
8. Peter (Acts 2:1, 13-41)
9. Noah (II Peter 2:5)
10. Philip (Acts 8:5-13)

74. PRIESTS

1. Potipherah (Gen. 41:45)
2. Jehoiada (II Kings 12:9)
3. Eleazar (Num. 20:25-28)
4. Ezra (Ezra 7)
5. Eli (I Sam. 2:11, 12)
6. Ahimelech (I Sam. 21:1-9)
7. Abiathar (I Sam. 22:18-20)
8. Urijah (II Kings 16:10, 11)
9. Aaron (Exod. 28)
10. Caiaphas (John 11:49-53)

75. PRISONERS

1. Barabbas (Mark 15:7-15)
2. Paul & Silas (Acts 16:25, 26)
3. Jeremiah (Jer. 38:6-13)
4. Three (Gen. 42:13-17)
5. Jehoiachin (Jer. 52:31)
6. Samson (Judg. 16:20, 21)
7. Peter (Acts 12:5-11)
8. Joseph (Gen. 41:14, 15)
9. John the Baptist (Matt. 14:3)

76. PROPHETS

1. Ezekiel (Ezek. 8:3)
2. Zechariah (Zech. 6:1-3)
3. Obadiah
4. Elisha (II Kings 2:22, 23)
5. Amos (Amos 7:14)
6. Jeremiah (Jer. 20:1, 2)
7. Isaiah (Isa. 38:21)
8. Jonah (Jonah 1:17)
9. Elijah (II Kings 2:11)
10. Daniel (Dan. 6:16)

77. QUEENS

1. c (I Kings 19:1, 2)
2. e (Acts 8:27)
3. g (I Kings 14:2-4)
4. f (Acts 25:23)
5. i (II Kings 11:1, 2)
6. h (I Kings 10:1-3)
7. b (Esther 2:7, 17)
8. j (I Kings 15:13)
9. d (Esther 1:10-19)
10. a (I Kings 2:19)

78. RUNNERS

1. Paul (I Cor. 9:24)
2. Abraham (Gen. 18:6)
3. Mary Magdalene (John 20:1, 2)
4. Ahimaaz & Cushi (II Sam. 18:19-23)
5. Asahel (II Sam. 2:18)
6. Philip (Acts 8:26-30)
7. Zacchaeus (Luke 19:2-4)
8. Samuel (I Sam. 3:4, 5)
9. Rebekah (Gen. 24:15, 19, 20)
10. Esau (Gen. 33:1, 4)

79. SCRIBES

1. Jonathan (I Chron. 27:32)
2. Shebna (II Kings 19:1, 2)
3. Jesus (Matt. 23:1-33)
4. Shimshai (Ezra 4:8)
5. Shaphan (II Kings 22:8)
6. Zadok (Neh. 13:13)
7. Jeiel (II Chron. 6:11)
8. Baruch (Jer. 36:4)
9. Ezra (Neh. 8:1-4)
10. Haman (Esther 3:12, 13)

80. SERVANTS

1. Eliezer (Gen. 15:2, 24)
2. Doeg (I Sam. 22:9, 18)
3. Malchus (John 18:10)
4. Hagar (Gen. 21:9, 10)
5. Gehazi (II Kings 5:20-26)
6. Rhoda (Acts 12:13-16)
7. Joseph (Gen. 39:2-6)
8. Phurah (Judg. 7:9-11)
9. Ziba (II Sam. 9:2, 10)
10. Onesimus (Philem. 1:10-16)

81. SINGERS

1. Paul & Silas (Acts 16:25)
2. Israelites (Exod. 32:4, 6, 18)
3. Solomon (I Kings 4:32)
4. Mount of Olives (Mark 14:26)
5. Josiah (II Chron. 35:23, 25)
6. Deborah and Barak (Judg. 5)
7. Jehoshaphat (II Chron. 20:17-21)
8. Moses (Exod. 15:1)
9. Case lots (I Chron. 25:7, 8)

82. SOLDIERS

1. Cornelius (Acts 10)
2. Deborah (Judg. 4:4-10)
3. Abishai (II Sam. 21:15-17)
4. Vinegar (Luke 23:36)
5. Julius (Acts 27)
6. Uriah (II Sam. 11:14, 15)
7. Eliab (I Sam. 17:20, 28)
8. One year (Deut. 24:5)
9. Jonathan (I Sam. 14:4-13)
10. Eleazar (I Chron. 11:12-14)

83. SONS

1. c (I Sam. 20:34)
2. e (Gen. 25:28)
3. g (I Tim. 1:2; II Tim. 1:2)
4. f (II Sam. 15:5-12)
5. i (Gen. 27:1-27)
6. h (II Chron. 15:16)
7. b (Exod. 2:10)
8. j (Gen. 4:17)
9. d (Luke 15:18, 19)
10. a (Gen. 46:29)

84. THIEVES

1. Micah (Judg. 17:1, 2)
2. Barabbas (Matt. 27:11-26)
3. Rachel (Gen. 31:19)
4. Achan (Josh. 7:20, 21)
5. Five (Judg. 18:17, 18)
6. Shishak (I Kings 14:25, 26)
7. Men of Shechem (Judg. 9:25)
8. Judas Iscariot (John 12:4-6)
9. Paul (II Cor. 11:8)
10. Benjamin (Gen. 44:1-12)

85. TRAVELERS

1. Elisha (II Kings 2:2-7)
2. Ruth (Ruth 1:18, 19)
3. Barnabas (Acts 13:2-4)
4. Jesus (Luke 24:13-15)
5. Jacob (Gen. 46:2-27)
6. Joseph (Matt. 2:19-23)
7. Abram & Lot (Gen. 12:1-5)
8. Jesus' 12 disciples (Luke 9:1-3)
9. Rebekah (Gen. 24:58-61)
10. Ten (Gen. 42:2, 3)

86. UNFAMILIAR PEOPLE

1. Seth (Gen. 4:25)
2. Orpah (Ruth 1:14, 15)
3. Dinah (Gen. 30:21)
4. Peninnah (I Sam. 1:2, 6)
5. Aholiab (Exod. 35:30-35)
6. Heber (Judg. 4:21)
7. Merab (I Sam. 18:17-19)
8. Keturah (Gen. 25:1)
9. Jehoshabeath (II Chron. 22:10-12)
10. Mahlon (Ruth 4:10)

87. WATCHERS

1. Moses' sister (Exod. 2:2-4)
2. Rizpah (II Sam. 21:8-10)
3. Pharisees (Mark 3:1-6)
4. Sisera's mother (Judg. 5:28)
5. Eli (I Sam. 1:9-12)
6. David (Ps. 102:7)
7. Mary Magdalene, Mary the mother of James the less and Joses, & Salome (Mark 15:40)
8. Isaiah (Isa. 21:6)
9. Peter, James, John (Mark 14:33-37)
10. Nehemiah (Neh. 7:3)

88. WEEPERS

1. David (II Sam. 15:30)
2. Jacob (Gen. 29:11)
3. Hezekiah (Isa. 38:3-5)
4. Peter (Matt. 26:74, 75)
5. Paul (Acts 20:37, 38)
6. Jesus (Luke 19:28, 41)
7. Ezekiel (Ezek. 24:15-18)
8. Saul (I Sam. 24:9-16)
9. Hannah (I Sam. 1:5-7)

89. WEALTHY PEOPLE

1. j (Gen. 26:12-15)
2. g (II Chron. 17:3-5)
3. h (I Sam. 25:2-11)
4. c (Matt. 19:21, 22)
5. i (Job 1:3, 17; 42:12)
6. a (II Chron. 32:27)
7. e (Gen. 13:2)
8. b (I Kings 10:23)
9. d (Luke 19:2)
10. f (Esther 1:1, 4)

90. WIVES

1. c (Esther 1:3, 11, 12)
2. h (I Kings 21:7)
3. j (I Sam. 19:11-17)
4. g (I Sam. 25:14-19)
5. f (Esther 5:14)
6. i (Gen. 12:11-15)
7. e (Acts 5:1-10)
8. a (Judg. 1:12, 13)
9. b (Gen. 24:51-66)
10. d (Gen. 3:1-6, 17)